Diwali

How the Festival of Lights came about

by Sam and Mat Dixon-Szul
edited by Alison Hedger

'With thanks to David Jordan, Paul Stevens and Tim Cotterill for all their help.'

illustrations by Hilary Lack

A new musical retelling the dramatic Indian epic poem,
The Ramayana – the triumph of good over evil.
To promote understanding of the Hindu faith, and Eastern culture, art and music.

A combination of live performance and shadow puppetry.
Ages 8-14 years

(Shadow puppets can be omitted if preferred. Alternatively,
the musical can be presented using only the shadow puppets.)

Duration: approximately 35 minutes.
CD with demonstration and backing tracks included.

SONGS

Authentic Indian musical devices are included where appropriate,
with suggested listening examples given.

1.	Ramayana	All (with descant)
2.	Everyone's Favourite Prince	All
3.	We're Going On An Adventure	Rama, Lakshmana and Viswamithra + All
4.	Rama Holds The Bow	Rama + All
5.	Shoop Be Dooby Doo-Wah	Kaikeyi + All
6.	Watch Out Sita!	Soorpanaka + All
7.	I'm Gonna Slice Him	Ravana's Ten Heads + All
8.	He's A Monkey Man	All
9.	Boo To The Losers	Monkeys, Goblins, Ravana + All
10.	It's Diwali	All (2-part harmony)

TEACHER'S BOOK complete with CD, production notes and music.

The script is in the separate Pupil's Book GA11418

A licence should be obtained from the publishers for performances of this work

© Copyright 2003 Golden Apple Productions
A division of Chester Music Limited
8/9 Frith Street, London W1D 3JB

Order No. GA11407
ISBN 0-7119-9785-3

EDUCATIONAL NOTES

Hindus, The Ramayana story and Diwali

No single essential belief or text makes a person a Hindu, but all Hindus share in the idea of overcoming the death and re-birth cycle. Hence Hindus strive to attain *moksha*, the liberation from this cycle. This may be through meditation so achieving wisdom, through actions following one's duty, or through dedication and devotion. Each way involves overcoming the hold of the self, the senses and worldly things. Included in the long tradition of famous Hindu teachers, is **Mohandas Gandhi** (died 1948), a name probably familiar with most people.

Besides worshipping in highly ornate and beautiful temples, Hindus have a shrine in the home where families are able to pray daily. The Hindu year is marked by special festivals devoted to gods or goddesses, and making a pilgrimage is another important part of Hindu worship.

Diwali (often spelt Divali) is the Indian autumn Festival of Lights. To celebrate this happy and colourful festival Hindus light lanterns to symbolise the victory of light (good) over dark (evil). Garlands decorate homes, presents are given and received and people wear their best clothes. Many send greeting cards and make a point of keeping in touch with their family. The goddess of good fortune, **Lakshmi**, is worshipped and the celebrations recall the Indian mythology of **Prince Rama** and **Sita's** homecoming after defeating the horrid, evil ten-headed beast **Ravana**. Everything to do with *Diwali* expresses the purity of good triumphing over evil.

This musical is based on the great Indian epic poem, **The Ramayana**. The original Sanskrit was written by a man called **Valmiki** about 3,000 years ago. It was very long indeed, having 24,000 verses. The exciting, deeply spiritual and moral story has been retold throughout the centuries and helps to explain the *Diwali* festival of lights. The script to this musical is also in verse, and aims to echo the sentiments of the original. Evil demons, super-heroes and heroines battle together in the story of good versus evil.

Ravana – An evil monster with ten heads and twenty arms, too strong to be overcome by any god.
Sita – A devoted and pure wife to Rama, who saw her birth as a result of her father ploughing the soil – hence her name means a furrow.
Monkey Army – An army of monkeys fighting for good, led by **Hanuman**, the magical monkey god.

Sam and Mat Dixon-Szul hope DIWALI will promote tolerance and interest in our multi-cultural society and be used as a springboard to explore other aspects of Eastern culture, art, music and religion.

CAST LIST

# indicates solo or specific group singing
§ indicates non-speaking part

THE GOOD GUYS

King Dasaratha (da-sa-raa-ta)	Kind ruler of Ayodhya
§**Queen Kausalya** (kow-saal-ya)	King Dasaratha's wife and Rama's mother
§**Queen Sumithra** (soo-mee-tra)	King Dasaratha's second wife and Lakshmana's and Sathrugna's mother

Rama
Lakshmana
§ **Sathrugna** (sa-troog-na)
  Bharatha (ba-ra-ta)

King Dasaratha's four sons

# **Viswamithra** (vee-swa-mee-tra)	A holy man
§ **Sita** (see-ta)	Rama's beautiful wife
Sita's Dad	King of another land
Hanuman (ha-noo-man)	Magic monkey man

THE BADDIES

# **Kaikeyi** (ki-kay-yee)	King Dasaratha's youngest wife and Bharatha's mother
# **Soorpanaka** (soor-pa-na-ka)	Forest dwelling evil demon with long big ears and a fantastically long nose
# **Ravana**	Soorpanaka's brother with ten heads! The most evil demon of all (*10 children*)

OTHER CHARACTERS/PARTICIPANTS

Narrators	Allocate as appropriate

    The gods
    Town People
§ # **The Monkey Army**
§ # **Army of evil Goblins**
  § **Forest** (*wear special tree hats*)

Doubling up of parts is possible
and some can be taken by the choir

Shadow Puppet Operators	Black outfits advisable
Choir	Sing at places marked "**All**"
Musicians	

SHADOW PUPPETS

The Hindus of South West Asia use puppet shadow-play theatre to tell The Ramayana story. So that children can explore the broadest potential of The Ramayana's culturally explosive theme, Sam and Mat Dixon-Szul have combined live performance and shadow puppetry. Helping to design and make shadow puppets and learning how to use them to maximum effect is a fun support activity.

Thai shadow puppets are usually drawn with the head in profile and the body and shoulders facing the front. They have one moveable arm. Fingers are elongated and the bodies are intricately cut to highlight figure patterns. Try inventing new characters and making a shadow puppet of them; a hole puncher can be very useful for decorative perforations. Accompany the puppets with Indian bells or similar chimes, and play them softly whilst the puppets are visible by the audience. Suggestions for puppet performance are given in the script and suggested puppet outlines are given at the back of the Pupil's book. If you decide to dispense with shadow puppets and concentrate on performing the musical in a more traditional way, the overall effect will not be disappointing. The script and music are very strong and stand alone. Alternatively, it may appeal to you to only use shadow puppetry for your performance.

SHADOW PUPPETRY

Refer to the drawings in the Pupil's Book for character idiosyncrasies.

In Indonesian shadow puppet plays, the *dalang* (master puppeteer) sits at arm's length behind a cloth screen. A paraffin pressure lamp gives light, and the puppets are made of leather. For your production you can achieve the same effect.

- Strap a white sheet tightly to the top half of a sturdy frame, and cover the bottom half with a thick piece of dark material. This will provide an area for the children to crouch in unseen.
- Position strong electric lights so that they shine behind the top white half of the screen.
- The puppets are held up against the back of the top white half of the screen, but the children remain low down, so as not to have their body shadows visible from the front.
- To achieve the best result, the room should be dark and the images moved slowly.
- Use thick card for the puppets, making them any size you decide; even life size perhaps? Each has a stick handle flat along the back so making the images reversible. Any floppy parts of the puppets can be reinforced with lollipop sticks.
- Everything else, including suitable sound effects are left to the imagination.

PROPS

- Bowl of rice
- 4 dolls for baby boys
- The Shiva bow (very large)
- Oversized feathered arrow
- Pair of sandals (part of Rama's costume)
- A throne, which can be a cushion on a stool
- Cardboard knife for Soorpanaka

COSTUMES and MASKS

Face masks are needed for the **Monkey and Goblin Armies**.
In addition, **Soorpanaka** needs a mask with a very long removable nose on elastic, as shown below.
The Forest is made up of children wearing hats suitably decorated with leaves.
Ravana the ten-headed demon needs just a simple cloth long enough to cover ten children. Each child has a hole in which to pass their heads through. **Hanuman** the monkey man's costume is perhaps the most tricky. Ideally he would be half man from top to toe on one side, and monkey on the other side. So being able to be either man or monkey to the audience, depending on which way he was positioned. However, this is rather complicated to achieve, so perhaps he could be man from the waist down and monkey on the top half. He could be easily discerned from the other monkeys by wearing a crown.

MONKEY MASK   GOBLIN MASK   SOORPANAKA with long nose

INCIDENTAL MUSIC and SOUND EFFECTS

A band of musicians improvise suitable incidental music to accompany the action in the play. Try to imitate authentic sounding music, using as many Eastern oriental instruments that are available to you. The sound effects for the puppetry are also fun to devise and deliver.

SONG ONE # RAMAYANA

All (*plus vocal descant*)

Opening song; no cue

Indian music has a constant drone in the background, which is usually played on the *tambura* (four-stringed instrument). The first song begins with a similar 'drone' in the bass. The drone continues, whilst a single melody line is introduced, which then develops into the rhythmic pattern of the song. Try doubling up this rhythmic pattern with a *Dholak* drum or some *gongroos* (dancing bells worn around the performers ankles) for a really authentic Indian sound. *Indian Talking Drums* have strings/ropes attached to the skin of the drum that alter the pitch of the sound when squeezed. These make the typical 'boingy' drum sound, similar to the *tabla*.

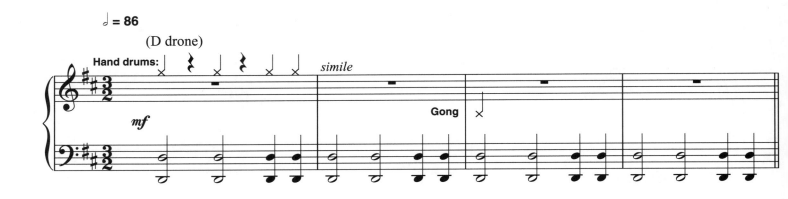

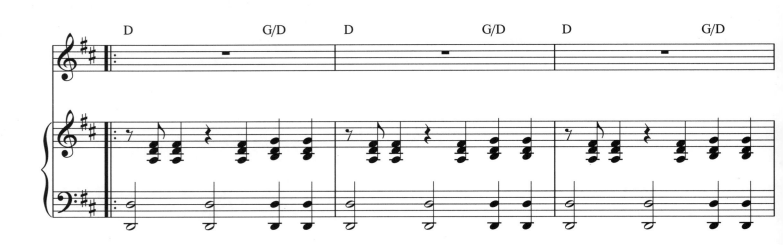

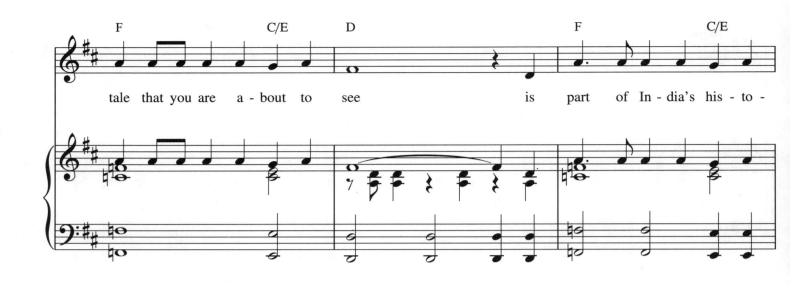

tale that you are a - bout to see   is part of In - dia's his - to -

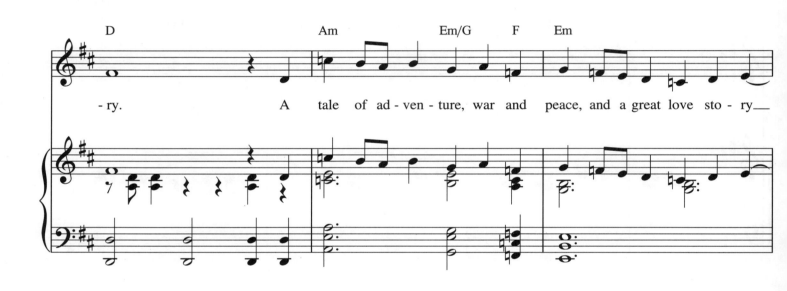

- ry.   A   tale of ad - ven - ture, war and   peace, and a great love sto - ry__

__   of good fight - ing

ev - il. Be - lieve all the things you see.

SONG TWO   EVERYONE'S FAVOURITE PRINCE

All

Cue: And the people loved him more.

In the Hindu religion Rama is thought to be an incarnation of the god 'Vishnu'. Vishnu is one of the most important of the Hindu gods who watches over humanity and keeps people from harm. He is believed to have visited the earth in different forms at least eight times. In the form of Prince Rama, he stands for goodness and mercy.

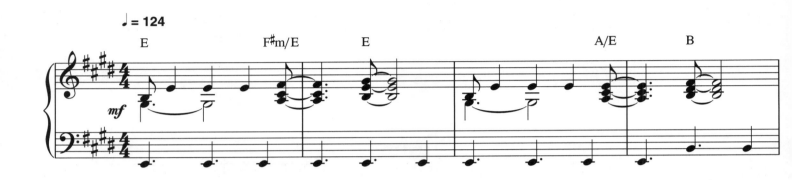

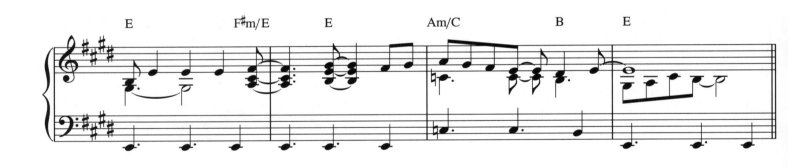

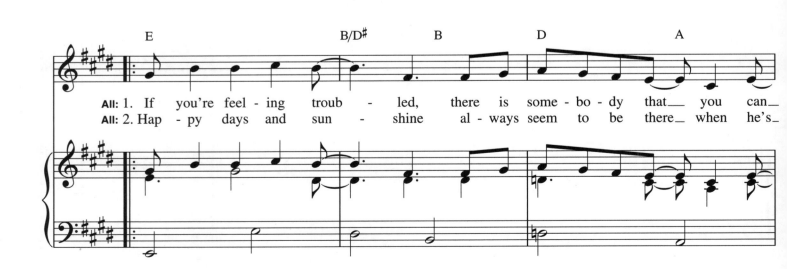

All: 1. If you're feel - ing troub - led, there is some - bo - dy that__ you can__
All: 2. Hap - py days and sun - shine al - ways seem to be there__ when he's

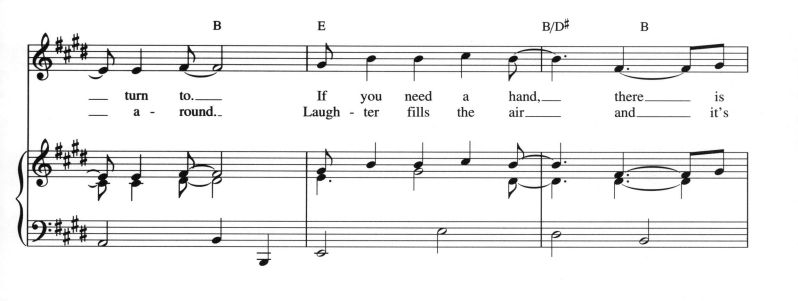

turn to.   If you need a hand, there is
a - round.   Laugh - ter fills the air and it's

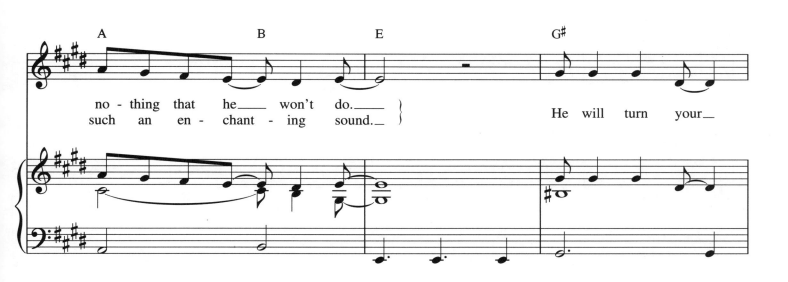

no - thing that he won't do.   He will turn your
such an en - chant - ing sound.

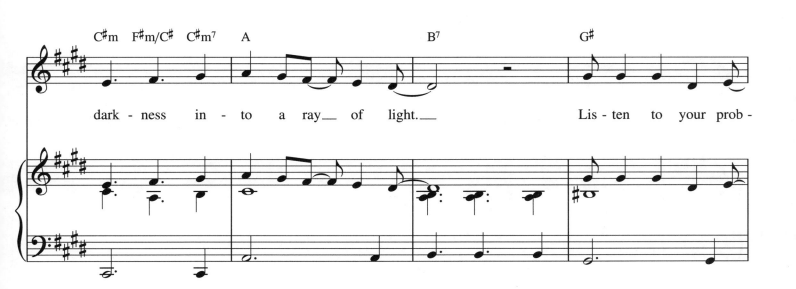

dark - ness in - to a ray of light.   Lis - ten to your prob -

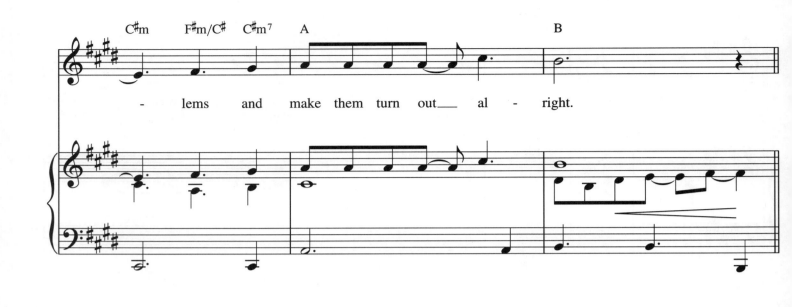

-lems and make them turn out____ al - right.

Chorus

Ra - ma has the ans - wer,____ Ra - ma has the ans - wer.____

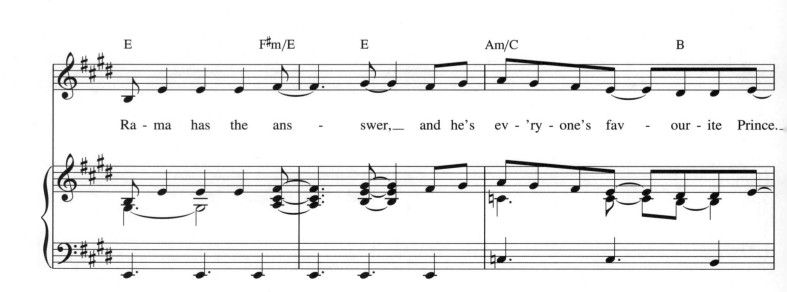

Ra - ma has the ans - wer,____ and he's ev - 'ry - one's fav - our - ite Prince.____

SONG THREE

WE'RE GOING ON AN ADVENTURE

Rama, Lakshmana, Viswamithra + All

Cue: The adventure had only just begun.

In North Indian classical music, the main identifiable feature is the 'raga', an intricate system of scales, which follow strictly defined boundaries. The performance of a raga begins with a slow introduction in free time, which introduces the notes of the raga one by one. This is called the 'alaap' and traditionally can last for several hours! This idea is used at the beginning of Song Three, where the five notes of B, C♯, E, F♯ and G are improvised over freely.

Suggested listening for full examples of a raga: *Ravi Shankar – Pandit Ravi Shankar (Ocora, France)* or *Lakshmi Shankar – Les Heures et les Saisons (Ocora, France).*
Both available on CD.

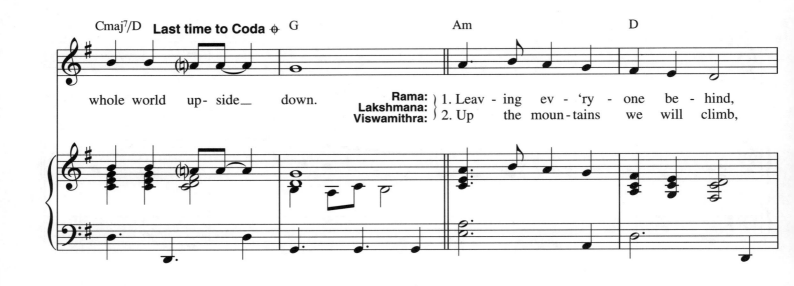

whole world up-side— down.

Rama:
Lakshmana:
Viswamithra:

1. Leav - ing ev - 'ry - one be - hind,
2. Up the moun - tains we will climb,

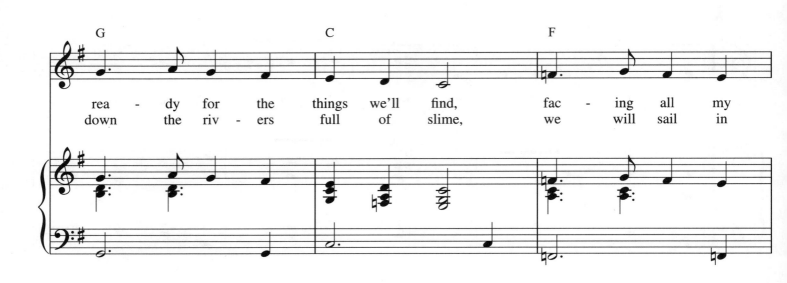

rea - dy for the things we'll find, fac - ing all my
down the riv - ers full of slime, we will sail in

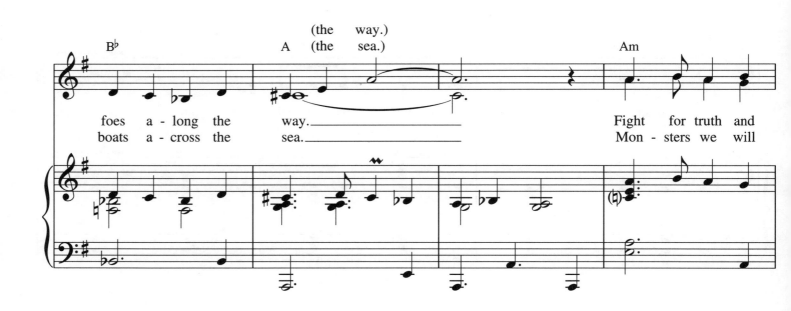

(the way.)
(the sea.)

foes a - long the way._____ Fight for truth and
boats a - cross the sea._____ Mon - sters we will

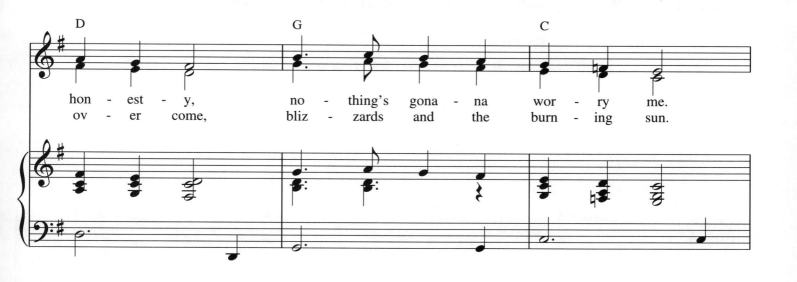

honest — y, no — thing's gona — na wor — ry me.
ov — er come, bliz — zards and the burn — ing sun.

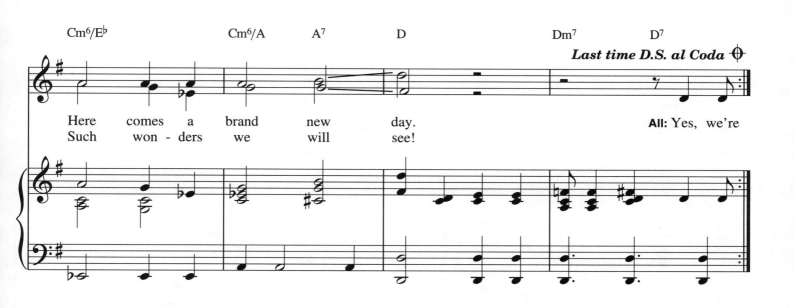

Last time D.S. al Coda

Here comes a brand new day.
Such won — ders we will see!

All: Yes, we're

Coda

down. We'll turn this whole world up — side — down!

SONG FOUR

RAMA HOLDS THE BOW

Rama + All

Cue: But if YOU can, then Sita will be yours!

Rama: 1. I've been on a jour - ney, feel - ing so a - lone.
All: 2. Ra - ma holds the bow and takes a gi - ant breath,

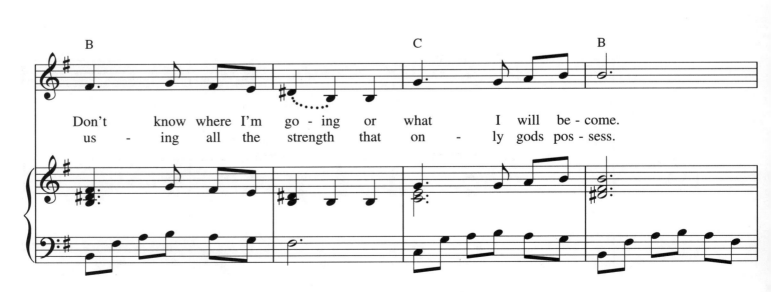

Don't know where I'm go - ing or what I will be - come.
us - ing all the strength that on - ly gods pos - sess.

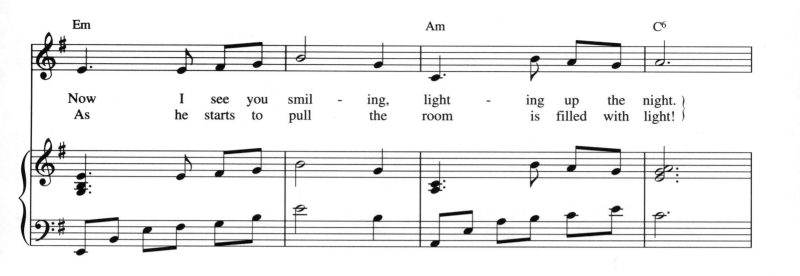

Now I see you smil - ing, light - ing up the night.
As he starts to pull the room is filled with light!

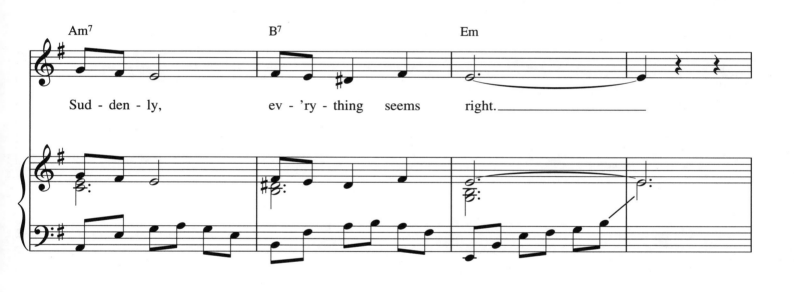

Sud - den - ly, ev - 'ry - thing seems right._____

Chorus

All: Can he pass the test and hope to win her hand,

now that fate has brought him to this for - eign land?

Why should he suc - ceed when ev - 'ry - one has failed?

Give__ him the strength to pull the bow._____

D.C. al **FINE**

Coda

mf

dim. al fine

FINE

20

SONG FIVE
SHOOP BE DOOBY DOO-WAH

Kaikeyi + All

Cue: For fourteen years, on a hopeless quest!

In the story of The Ramayana, Queen Kaikeyi is the youngest of the King's three wives. She is hot headed and her ambitious nature makes her behave badly. However Rama does not see her as a bad person because he knows that her actions will help to shape his own destiny and enable him to do great things.

Shoop be doo-by doo-wah,__ she's oh so an - gry. She's

cooked her goose__ and lost the plot,__ she's turn - ing bad.__

Kaikeyi: 1. All these years I thought I'd see my son Bha-ra-tha as the King.
2. But my wish can still come true, I on - ly have to ask the King.

Now my hus - band choo - ses Ra - ma, all my hopes don't mean a thing.
Long a - go he made a pro - mise he would grant me an - y - thing.

Chorus

All: Shoop be doo-by doo-wah,__ she's go-ing cra-zy! Shoop be doo-by doo-wah,__ she's

real-ly__ mad. Shoop be doo-by doo-wah,__ she's oh so an-gry. She's

cooked her goose__ and lost the plot,__ she's turn-ing bad.__ **Kaikeyi:** Oh yes I'm

SONG SIX

WATCH OUT SITA!

Soorpanaka + All (*in two parts*) with perhaps some shouts from Ravana

Cue: Look out Sita, beware!

The rhythm of Song Six follows a 'Dum Tickey Dum Tickey' Bhangra style beat. The Bhangra style originated from the drum-based, dance music of the farmers in the Punjab. The crop they farmed was very often 'hemp' (bhang) and that is how the style got its name. It has now become a modem British-Asian pop music style.

Suggested listening for examples of Bhangra: *Safri Boys – Bomb Thumbi (Roma Music Bank, UK)* or *DCS – Bhangra's Gonna Get You (Multitone, UK).* Both available on CD.

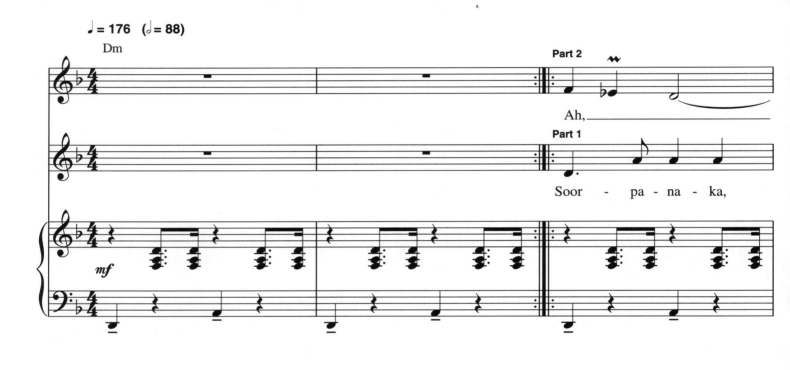

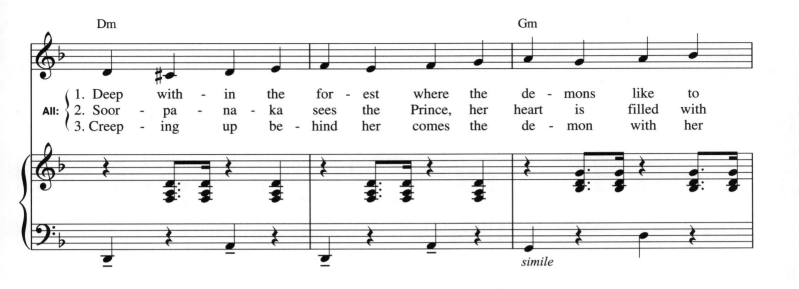

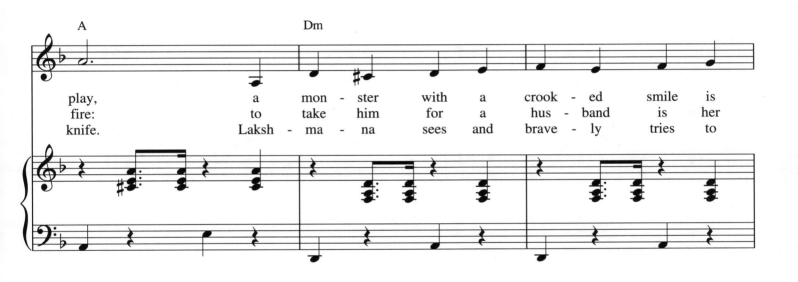

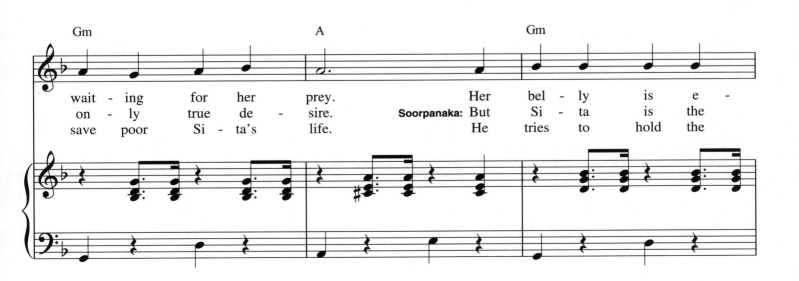

27

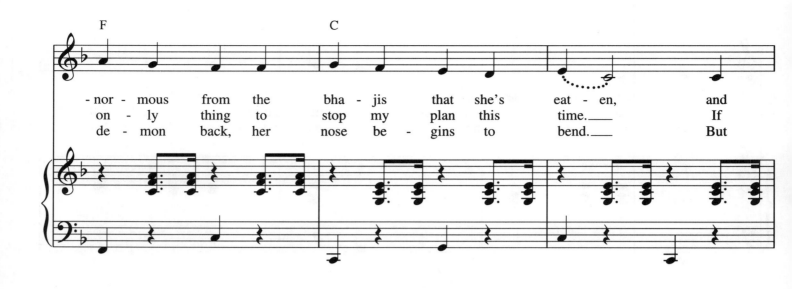

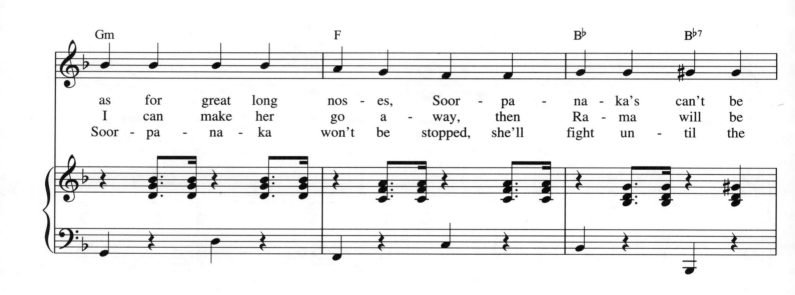

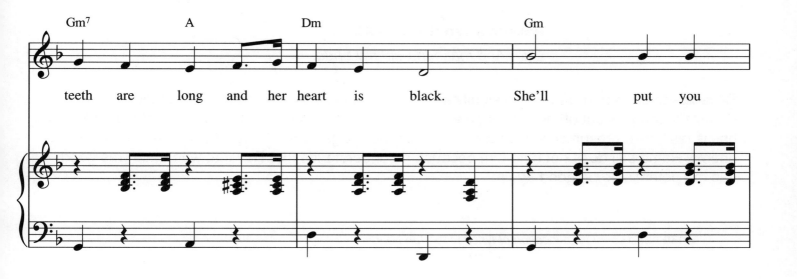

teeth are long and her heart is black. She'll put you

in a sack and have you for her din - ner!

D.C. for verses 2 and 3

Repeat chorus once more at end
getting faster and faster

29

I'M GONNA SLICE HIM

Ravana's Ten Heads + All

Cue: And make the girl my bride.

Ravana's ten heads have special significance in The Ramayana. The story says that if one of Ravana's heads is cut off he simply grows another one in its place! The only weak spot that Ravana has is his heart, presumably because it is full of bad things. Even though Ravana is Rama's worst enemy, Rama still does not hate him because he understands that Ravana, who once was good, has the potential to be good again.

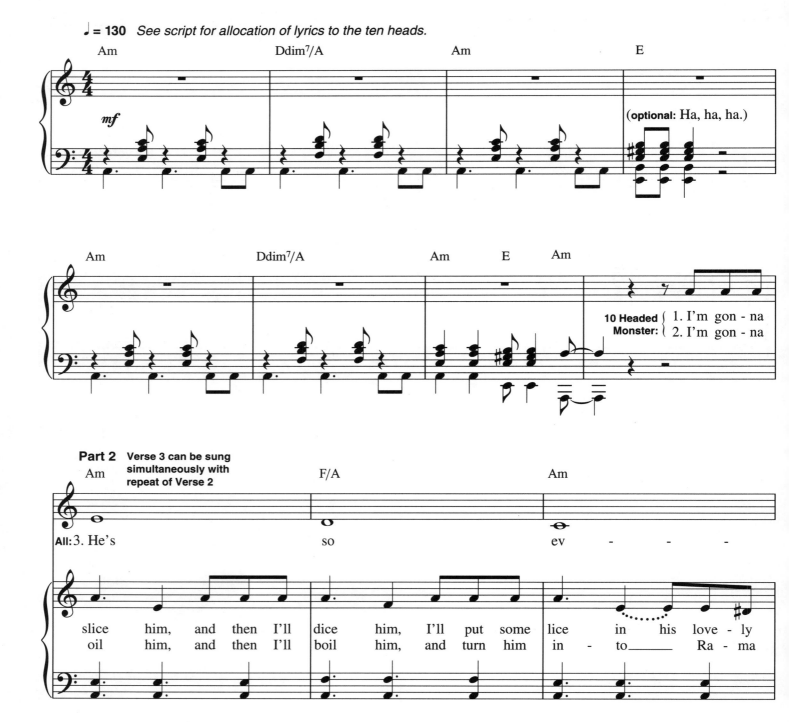

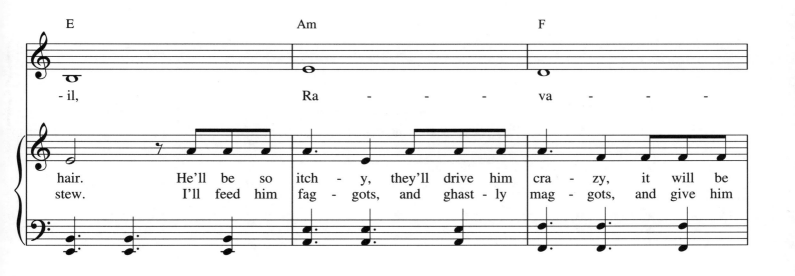

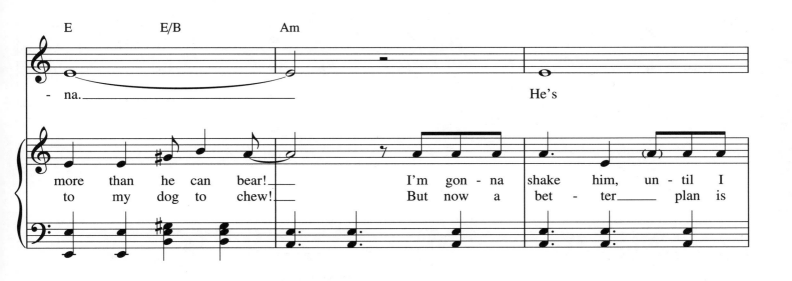

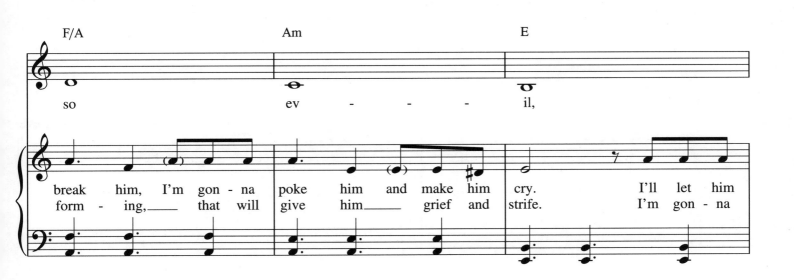

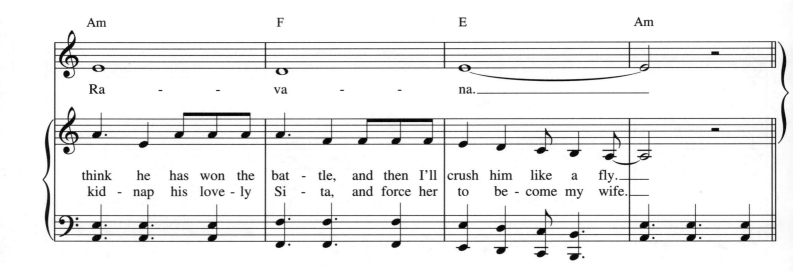

Ra - va - - na.

think he has won the bat - tle, and then I'll crush him like a fly.
kid - nap his love - ly Si - ta, and force her to be - come my wife.

Chorus

All: When it comes to ev - il plans___ Ra - va - na is sec - ond to none.

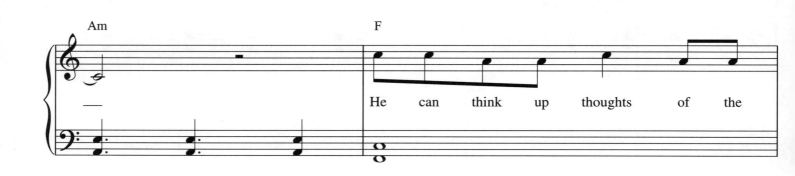

___ He can think up thoughts of the

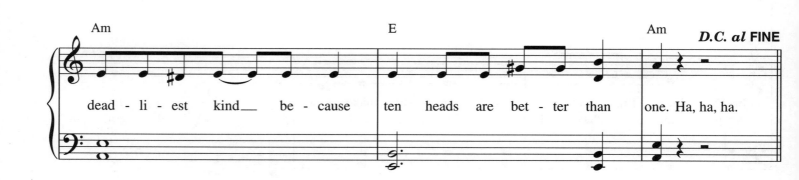

D.C. al **FINE**

dead - li - est kind___ be - cause ten heads are bet - ter than one. Ha, ha, ha.

Coda

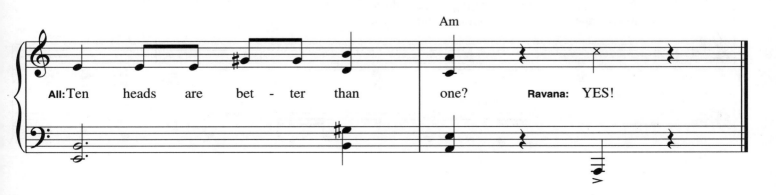

33

SONG EIGHT   HE'S A MONKEY MAN

All

Cue: Half monkey?

Hanuman is the courageous and loyal supporter of Prince Rama, even though he is the son of the god of wind and possesses his own magical powers. In paintings and pictures, Hanuman is often seen kneeling in front of Rama because he knows that Rama is a great god and he worships him. Hindus believe that meditating on Hanuman brings great inner strength and freedom from fear.

All: 1. If there is a rum - ble in the jun - gle,___
All: 2. Ha - nu - man is King of all the mon - keys,___

Ha - nu - man comes swing - ing through the trees.___
le - murs, apes, ba - boons and chim - pan - zees.___

34

He can put a stop to an - y trou - ble,____ sol - ving trick - y prob - lems is a
Ev - en big gor - il - las bow be - fore____ him,____ though he on - ly comes up to their

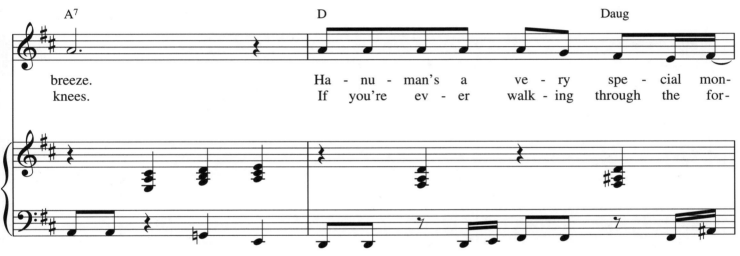

breeze. Ha - nu - man's a ve - ry spe - cial mon-
knees. If you're ev - er walk - ing through the for -

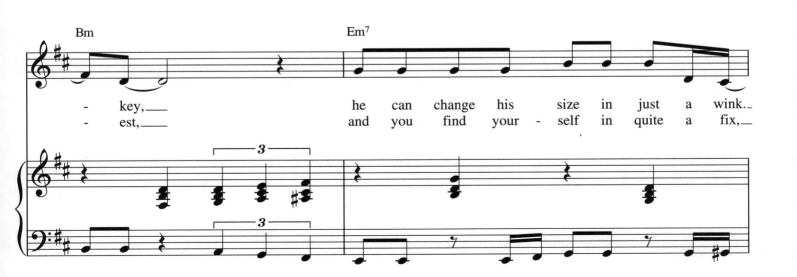

- key,____ he can change his size in just a wink.
- est,____ and you find your - self in quite a fix,____

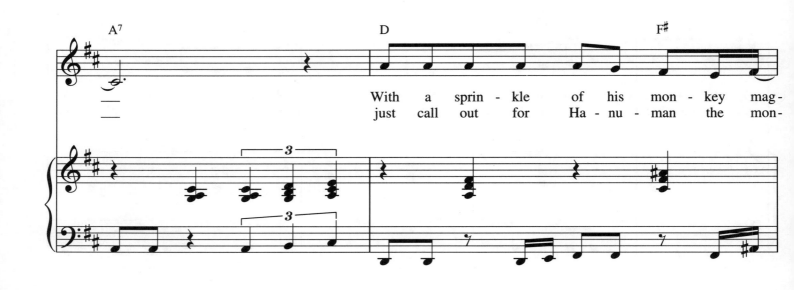

With a sprin-kle of his mon-key mag-
just call out for Ha-nu-man the mon-

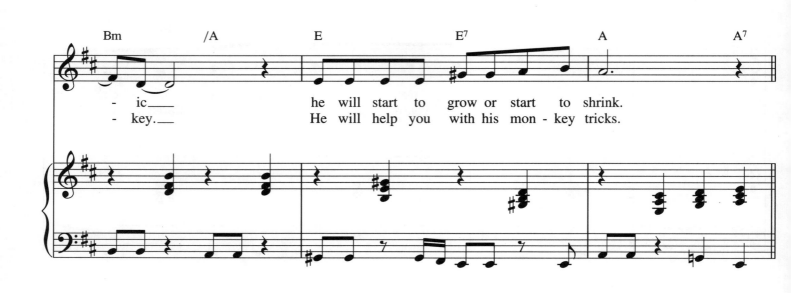

-ic___   he will start to grow or start to shrink.
-key.___   He will help you with his mon-key tricks.

Chorus

Whoo - hoo - hoo, he's a mon-key man,___   fear - less, kind and

strong. An al - most hu - man Ha - nu - man,— he's a

two foot high King Kong!

3. Ha - nu - man, the mon -
4. When he blinks his mon -

- key man, he can do what no one can. Cross the world in just
- key eyes, he will start to shrink in size. Now he's sit - ting un -

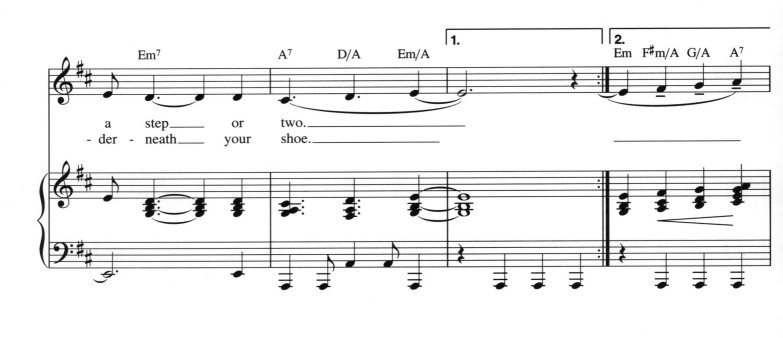

a step____ or two._____

-der - neath____ your shoe._____

Chorus

Whoo - hoo - hoo, he's a mon - key man,__ fear-less, kind and strong. An

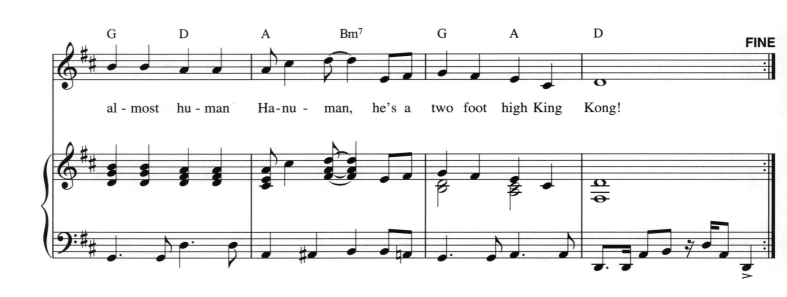

al - most hu - man Ha - nu - man, he's a two foot high King Kong!

FINE

SONG NINE   BOO TO THE LOSERS

Monkeys, Goblins, Ravana + All

Cue: We can all live in peace.

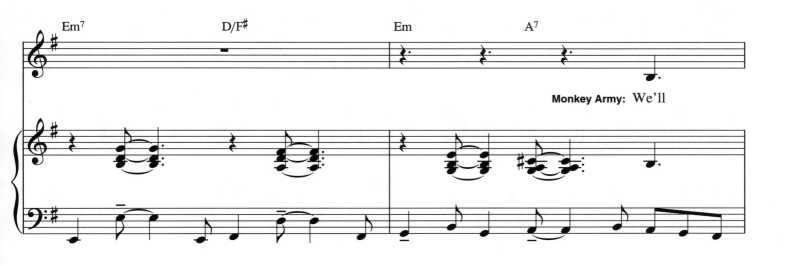

Monkey Army: We'll

Chorus

win, we'll win, we'll win this___ fight!___ Glo - ry, glo - ry to the

SONG TEN   IT'S DIWALI

All (*plus 2 part harmony*)

Cue: To start a happier life.

Diwali is a Hindu festival celebrated during the months of October and November. People decorate their homes with little lamps called 'Diyas'. In the story, Bharatha ordered a public holiday for the people to celebrate the return of Rama and Sita and all the buildings were brightly decorated with flowers and flags. Lanterns were lit to guide Rama and Sita through the town to the palace, where they were crowned King and Queen. This is why lanterns are lit during *Diwali* today, to remind us that light always chases away darkness.

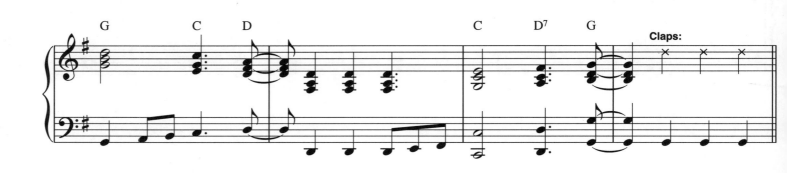

All: Here come Ra - ma and Si - ta. Ev - 'ry - bod - y go pre - pare the lamps.

let's all give a cheer.___ Hoo - ray!
Ra - ma is the King!___ Woo!___

47

CD Track Listing

Complete Songs (with vocals)

1. Ramayana
2. Everyone's Favourite Prince
3. We're Going On An Adventure
4. Rama Holds The Bow
5. Shoop Be Dooby Doo-Wah
6. Watch Out Sita!
7. I'm Gonna Slice Him
8. He's A Monkey Man
9. Boo To The Losers
10. It's Diwali

Complete Songs (without vocals)

11. Ramayana
12. Everyone's Favourite Prince
13. We're Going On An Adventure
14. Rama Holds The Bow
15. Shoop Be Dooby Doo-Wah
16. Watch Out Sita!
17. I'm Gonna Slice Him
18. He's A Monkey Man
19. Boo To The Losers
20. It's Diwali

Music arranged by Rick Cardinali. Vocals by Elly Barnes. CD recorded, mixed and mastered by Jonas Persson.